Number 1

1 2 3 4 5 6 7 8 9 10 11 12 13 14 15

A Count and write the number.

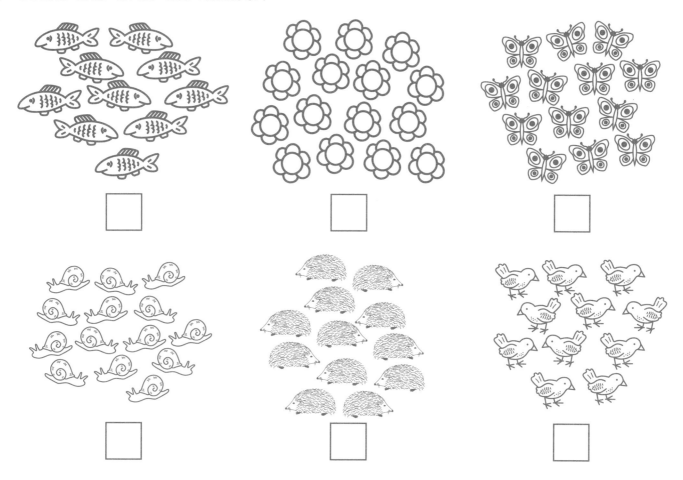

B Fill in the missing numbers.

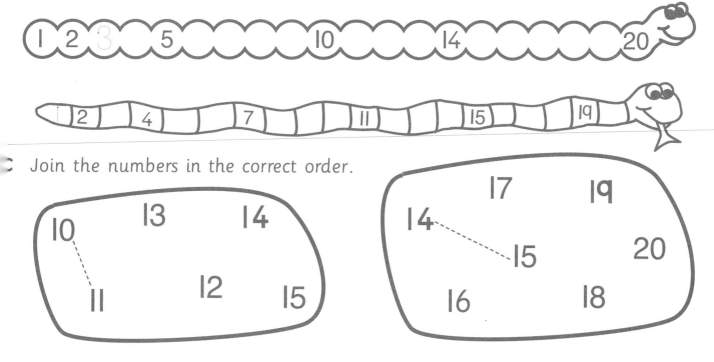

1 2 3 ◯ 5 ◯ ◯ ◯ ◯ 10 ◯ ◯ ◯ 14 ◯ ◯ ◯ ◯ ◯ 20

2 ◯ 4 ◯ ◯ 7 ◯ ◯ ◯ 11 ◯ ◯ ◯ 15 ◯ ◯ ◯ 19

C Join the numbers in the correct order.

10   13   14
11   12   15

17   19
14   15   20
16   18

3

Language 2

A Finish the story.
Write the words. Read the story.

squirrel   woods   dark   walk   called   tree   autumn acorns   noise   dog

Emma and Tom took Jip for a

_____

Jip ran ahead into the

_____

"Jip! Jip! Come back!" they

_____

They ran after him into the

_____ woods.

They heard a _____

Look it's a _____

Jip ran up and the squirrel ran up the

_____

Come here you bad _____

What do squirrels eat? _____   What time of year was it? _____

B Look at the pictures. Say the word for the picture. Listen to the first sound and write it down at the beginning of the word. **gl pl sl**

_ _ ug

_ _ ass

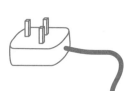

_ _ ug

_ _ edge

_ _ ipper

_ _ ate

_ _ ove

_ _ ant

Science 1

A What are the things in the kitchen made of?
Write the name of the materials.

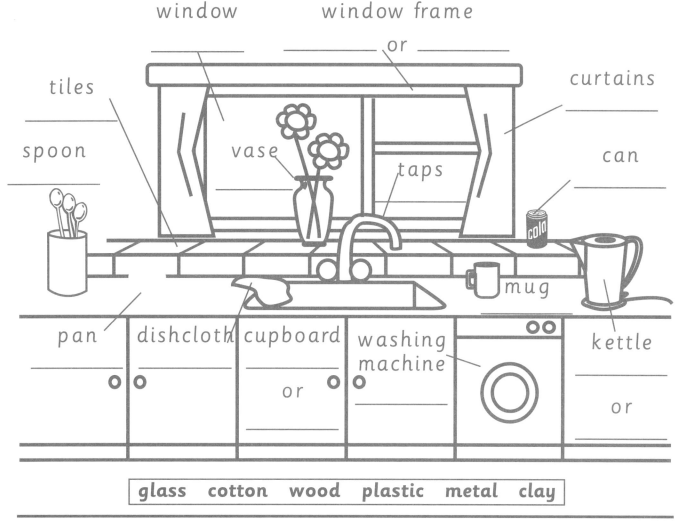

window

window frame

_____ or _____

tiles

spoon

vase

taps

curtains

can

mug

kettle

pan dishcloth cupboard washing machine

_____ _____ or _____ _____

or _____

| glass   cotton   wood   plastic   metal   clay |

B Sort these objects into two sets: those that are made from natural materials and those that are man-made.

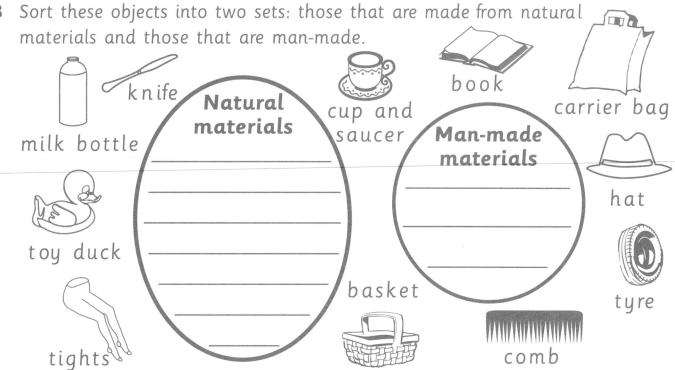

knife

Natural materials

cup and saucer

book

carrier bag

milk bottle

Man-made materials

hat

toy duck

tights

basket

comb

tyre

Language 3

A Finish the sentence using a word for the box.

| running hopping washing flying eating swimming |

This bird is _____

The rabbit is _____

This fish is _____

My cat is _____ herself.

Sam's tortoise is _____

This dog is _____ after the ball.

B Match the pictures that rhyme.
Say the word first.

Find a word to rhyme with...	
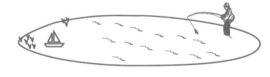 tree	
ant	
tent	
thumb	

Number 2

A Fill in the missing numbers.

1 ◇ 2 ◇ 3 ◇ 4 ◇ ◇ ◇ ◇ ◇ ◇ 10 ◇ ◇ ◇ 13 ◇ ◇ ◇ ◇ 17 ◇ ◇ ◇ ◇

B Count and write the number.

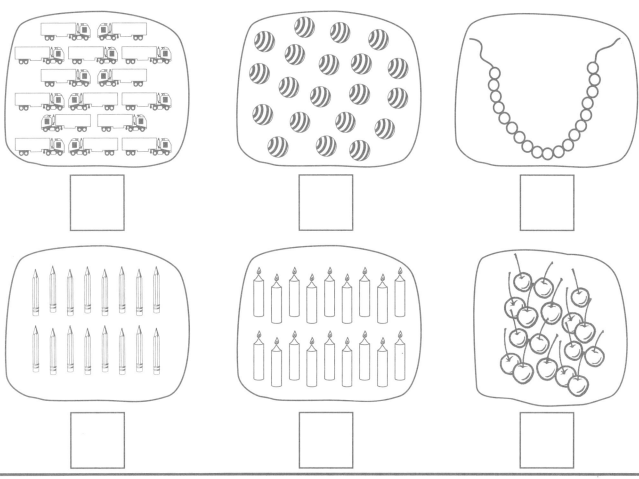

C Join the dots to draw a picture. Start at 1.

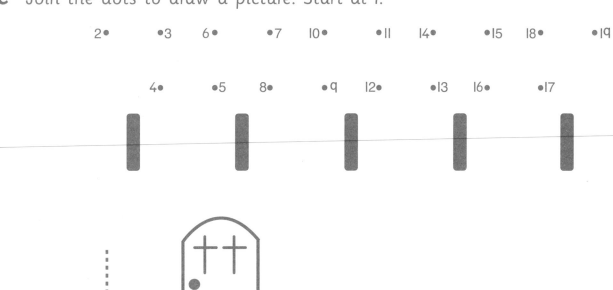

Language 4

A Read the clues. Everyone had salad. Dad had fish. Mum had a pizza. Jack had an apple and Sarah had fish and chips. Mum had a cup of tea. Add the person's name under each meal.

_____

_____

_____

_____

B Name the cutlery using the words from the box.

| fork   knife   spoon   teaspoon |

_____   _____   _____   _____

Answer the questions.

What do we use to cut food? _____

Name two things you eat with a spoon.

_____ _____

What do we use to stir the sugar? _____

8

Science 2

A Materials
Is it bendy or rigid? Colour the bendy things **blue** and the rigid things **red**.

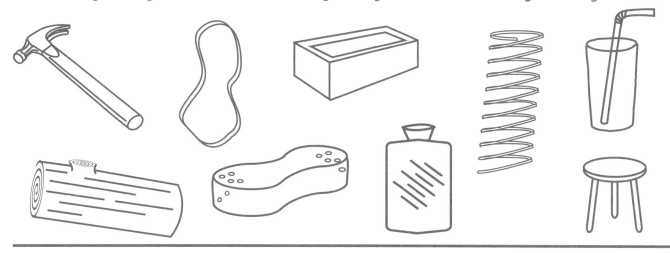

B Is it transparent or opaque? Map the picture to the correct word.

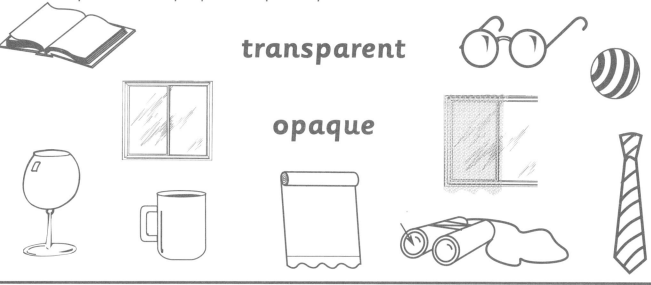

transparent

opaque

C Is it rough or smooth? Write **r** under anything rough and **s** under anything smooth.

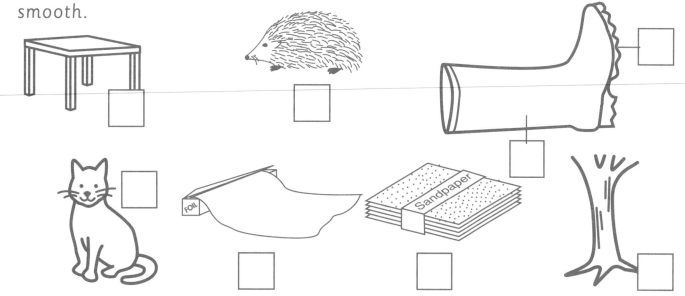

Number 3

A Use the number line to help you add.

```
0  1  2  3  4  5  6  7  8  9  10  11  12  13  14  15  16  17  18  19  20
```

15 + 1 = ☐	13 + 3 = ☐	15 + 2 = ☐
12 + 2 = ☐	16 + 2 = ☐	11 + 3 = ☐
18 + 2 = ☐	11 + 4 = ☐	13 + 5 = ☐
16 + 4 = ☐	12 + 3 = ☐	12 + 6 = ☐
11 + 5 = ☐	14 + 5 = ☐	14 + 3 = ☐

B Shopping

I buy	I spend	Show how you pay. Use 10p, 5p, 2p and 1p coins.
☐10☐p and ☐2☐p → ☐ p		(10p) (2p)
☐ p and ☐ p → ☐ p		
☐ p and ☐ p → ☐ p		
☐ p and ☐ p → ☐ p		

C Continue the pattern.

Language 5

A Town and Country

Which things are found in the town and which are found in the country? Write their names in the correct set.

| cows bank flats sheep |
| supermarket tractor fields factory |

Can you think of some things you would find in both the town and country?

B Look at the pictures. Say the word for the picture. Listen to the first sound and write it down at the beginning of the word. Join each picture to the correct sound-brick.

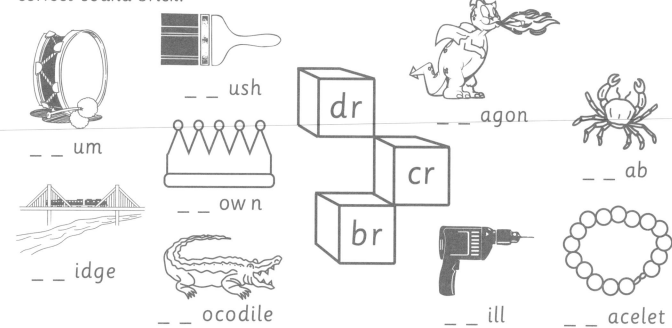

_ _ ush

dr

_ _ agon

_ _ um

cr

_ _ ab

_ _ own

br

_ _ idge

_ _ ocodile

_ _ ill

_ _ acelet

Number 4

A What are their names? Match the shapes to their names.

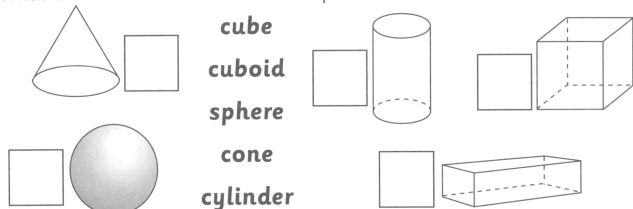

cube

cuboid

sphere

cone

cylinder

Write the number of faces each shape has in the box beside it.

B How much? Write the amount in each box.

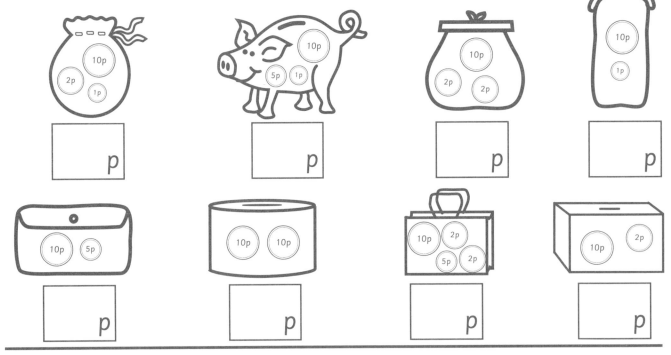

C Finish the number pattern.

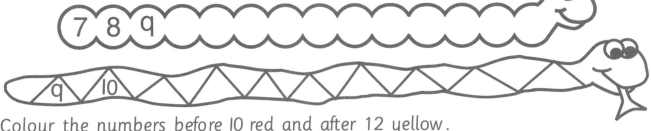

7 8 9

9 10

Colour the numbers before 10 red and after 12 yellow.

D Write the numbers after: | Write the numbers before:

Science 3

A Some materials change.
What happens when you add these to water? Write their names in the correct set.

salt   jelly   sugar   sand   soil   vinegar   oil

<u>dissolve</u>	<u>do not dissolve</u>

Do these things dissolve without being stirred? _____

B Some things change when you heat them and then change back when they cool. Colour blue the things that change when they are heated.
Draw a ring round each thing that changes back when cooled.

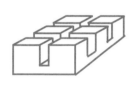   

What changes from liquid to solid? _____
When is butter easier to spread? _____

C Some things go harder when heated. Match to the correct word.

    **melt**   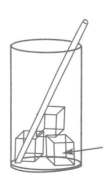

solidify

Language 6

Read about hedgehogs.

Hedgehogs are small animals. They live under hedges. Hedgehogs curl up into a ball if they are frightened. Hedgehogs eat worms, snails, slugs and spiders. They have hard spines on their backs. They cannot see very well but they have a good sense of smell.

A Answer these questions.

Where do hedgehogs live?

_____

Name two things hedgehogs eat.

_____

What can't they do very well? _____

B Look at the pictures. Say the word for the picture. Listen to the first sound. Join the picture to the correct sound. Write the sound under the picture.

14

EARLY HOMEWORK BOOK 3 ANSWERS

Note for users

Taking an interest in the child's work is of great importance. Take every opportunity to praise work that is correct, and offer help and advice where the child experiences difficulty. Make sure that the child understands the instructions that introduce each exercise. Some children experience more difficulty with the instructions than with the work itself.

There are advantages in allowing the child to mark his or her own work. This informs the child of the correct answer in cases where mistakes have occurred. It is important to look again at answers that are wrong and for the child to discover why an answer is incorrect so that he or she can learn as a result of the error.

Where a weakness is revealed, further similar exercises can be provided to give the child more practice and confidence.

A child should not be expected to undertake too much work in a short time. The exercises should be well spaced out so that the last pages are being worked towards the end of the appropriate school year.

Language 1   page 2

A   Lisa feeds hungry animals. Gary keeps animal homes clean. Mark teaches sea lions. Emma helps sick animals.

B   Emma   Mark
    Gary   Lisa

C   clap   flower   blow   flame
    blackbird   flag   claw   clown

Number 1   page 3

A   10   15   13
    14   12   11

B   3 4 6 7 8 9 11 12 13 15 16 17 18 19
    1 3 5 6 8 9 10 12 13 14 16 17 18 20

C
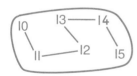   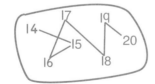

Language 2   page 4

A   walk
    woods
    called
    dark
    noise
    squirrel
    tree
    dog
    acorns
    autumn

B   slug   glass   plug   sledge
    slipper   plate   glove   plant

Science 1   page 5

A   window → glass
    window frame → wood/plastic
    vase → glass
    spoon → wood
    pan → metal
    dishcloth → cotton
    cupboard → wood/plastic
    taps → metal
    can → metal
    curtains → cotton
    tiles → clay
    mug → clay
    kettle → metal/plastic
    washing machine → metal

B   **Natural materials**   **Man-made materials**
    milk bottle   toy duck
    knife   tights
    cup and saucer   comb
    basket   carrier bag
    book
    hat
    tyre

Language 3   page 6

A   flying
    hopping
    swimming
    washing
    eating
    running

B

tree ➜ bee free
ant ➜ pant
tent ➜ bent
thumb ➜ plum

Number 2   page 7

A   5   6   7   8   9   11   12   14   15
        16   18   19   20

B   15   20   19
        16   18   17

C
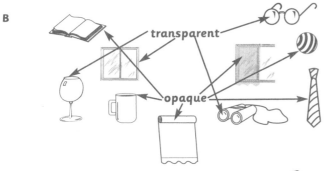

Language 4   page 8

A   Jack   Mum
        Dad   Sarah

B   teaspoon   knife   spoon   fork
        knife
        Answers variable.
        spoon

Science 2   page 9

A   <u>bendy</u> things - blue   <u>rigid</u> things - red
        rubber band   hammer
        spring   log
        hot water bottle   brick
        straw   stool
        sponge   glass

B
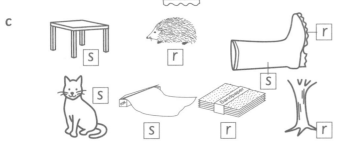

C

Number 3   page 10

A   16   16   17
        14   18   14
        20   15   18
        20   15   18
        16   19   17

B   10p and 2p → 12p   (10p)(2p)   or different value of coins

        5p and 4p → 9   (5p)(2p)(2p)   or different value of coins

        6p and 5p → 11   (10p)(1p)   or different value of coins

        8p and 6p → 14   (10p)(2p)(2p)   or different value of coins

C
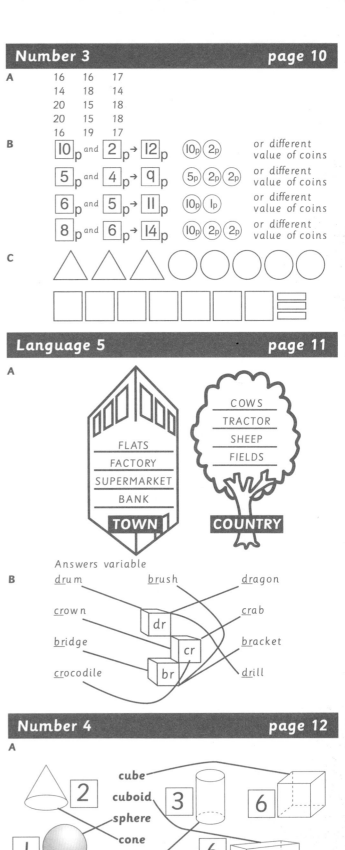

Language 5   page 11

A

TOWN: FLATS, FACTORY, SUPERMARKET, BANK

COUNTRY: COWS, TRACTOR, SHEEP, FIELDS

Answers variable

B   <u>dr</u>um   <u>br</u>ush   <u>dr</u>agon
        <u>cr</u>own   <u>cr</u>ab
        <u>br</u>idge   <u>br</u>acket
        <u>cr</u>ocodile   <u>dr</u>ill

Number 4   page 12

A
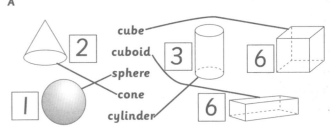

cube   cuboid   sphere   cone   cylinder

B   13p   16p   14p   11p
        15p   20p   19p   12p

C   red   yellow
        (8 9) 10 11 12   (13 14 15 16 17 18 19 20)
        red   yellow
        (9) 10 11 12   (13 14 15 16 17 18)

D   12   11   15 | 14   12   10
        18   16   20 | 17   15   19

Science 3 — page 13

A

dissolve	do not dissolve
salt	sand
vinegar	soil
sugar	oil
jelly	

no

B

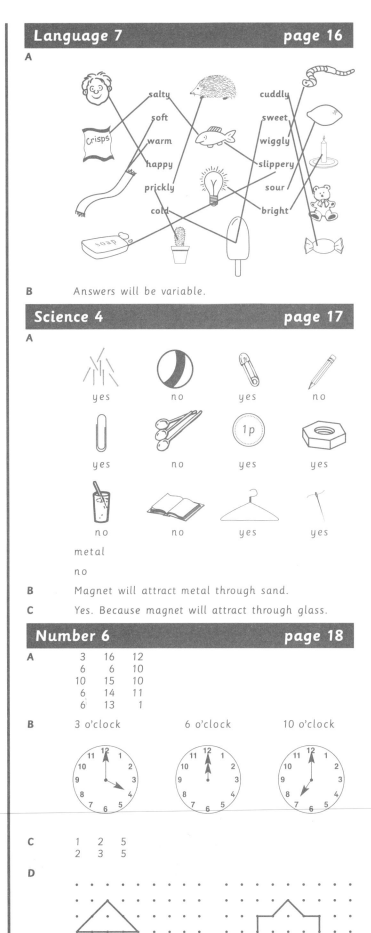

blue   blue   blue

jelly

when it is soft

C

melt

solidify

Language 6 — page 14

A
Under hedges.
Any 2 of these: worms snails, slugs, spiders
see

B

pr   pr
fr
gr   gr
tr
gr
fr   pr
fr   tr

Number 5 — page 15

A Estimates will be variable.
12   15   10   20

B

+10

12 18 2 8 19 9 6 16 14 4 1 11 17 7 10 20

-10

1 5 11 15 6 16 12 2 8 18 20 10 14 17 4 7

C

D Answers may be variable.
6 + 4   8 + 3   10 + 3
10 + 4   10 + 8   10 + 10

Language 7 — page 16

A

salty   cuddly
soft   sweet
warm   wiggly
happy   slippery
prickly   sour
cold   bright

Crisps   soap

B Answers will be variable.

Science 4 — page 17

A

yes   no   yes   no

yes   no   yes   yes

no   no   yes   yes

metal

no

B Magnet will attract metal through sand.

C Yes. Because magnet will attract through glass.

Number 6 — page 18

A
3   16   12
6   6   10
10 15   10
6   14   11
6   13   1

B   3 o'clock   6 o'clock   10 o'clock

C
1   2   5
2   3   5

D

Language 8 — page 19

A
bird   fish
frog   snake

tortoise/crocodile/newt/butterfly

B
ch<u>in</u>   <u>st</u>amp   <u>sh</u>ip   <u>ch</u>air

<u>st</u>ar   <u>sh</u>eep   <u>ch</u>eese   <u>st</u>airs

Number 7 — page 20

A
6   10   0
2   10   5
8   0   3
1   10   5

B

Row 1: 1p   1p   10p   20p   2p   5p
Row 2: 10p   2p   1p   5p   1p   20p
Row 3: 2p   2p   10p   20p   10p   1p
Row 4: 2p   2p   2p   1p   10p   20p

C
12 butterflies   15 birds
8 butterflies on the flowers   10 birds on the rooftop
4 butterflies in the air   5 birds flying around
8 + 4 = 12   10 + 5 = 15

Science 5 — page 21

A
Coloured yellow: nylon wool cotton paper
kitchen towel tissue newspaper cardboard

Plastic and tinfoil

B
canvas/nylon   wool   nylon   leather

paper   nylon   feathers   plastic

Wood or plastic

Because it would be waterproof and it would float

Language 9 — page 22

A
Answers variable but could include:
I can see an elephant.
The elephant is beating a drum.
It is night time.
The owl is in the tree.
Little Red Riding Hood is walking along.
She is carrying a basket of food.
It is daytime.
She is in the woods.

B
pram   stool   drum   flag
glass   sleep   frog   chop

Number 8 — page 23

A
9   10   4
16   12   20
11   20   8
13   16   10
2   11   20

B
Answers variable.

C
Tuesday   Wednesday
Monday   Sunday
Thursday   Friday

Sunday   Answer variable
Saturday

Language 10 — page 24

A
No
No
Yes
A fox
At night

Number 9 — page 25

A
Answers variable.

B
Answers variable.
4

C
2 tens and   1 ten and   2 tens and
6 ones = 26   8 ones = 18   4 ones = 24

3 tens and   Draw the beads   Draw the beads
7 ones = 37   **27**   **14**

2 tens and   1 ten and
7 ones = 27   4 ones = 14

D
40   50   60   80   90   100

Science 6 — page 26

A
red orange yellow green blue indigo violet
green
indigo

B
purple
green
orange
pink
they go lighter

Number 10 — page 27

A
30
2
13
black
4

B
15 7 18 / 10 8 16 / 3 14
5 / 9
2 13 / 12 4 10 / 6 17 11

C
$\frac{1}{2}$ past 9 $\frac{1}{2}$ past 6 $\frac{1}{2}$ past 4 $\frac{1}{2}$ past 11 $\frac{1}{2}$ past 12

Number 5

A Estimate the number in each set. Then count and write the number.

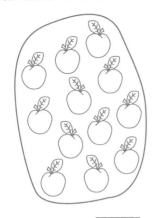  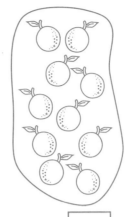 

Estimate ☐   Estimate ☐   Estimate ☐   Estimate ☐

Number ☐   Number ☐   Number ☐   Number ☐

B Adding 10.   Taking away 10.

Hexagons

C Colour all the hexagons blue. Join the hexagons.

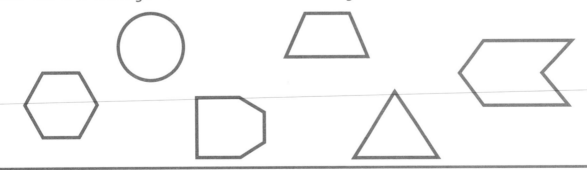

D

6 3 8
4
10 12

Use any 2 numbers to make the sum.

☐ + ☐ → 10   ☐ + ☐ → 11   ☐ + ☐ → 13

☐ + ☐ → 14   ☐ + ☐ → 18   ☐ + ☐ → 20

Language 7

A Look at the pictures. Read the words.
Join each word to the picture it describes. Some will have more than one.

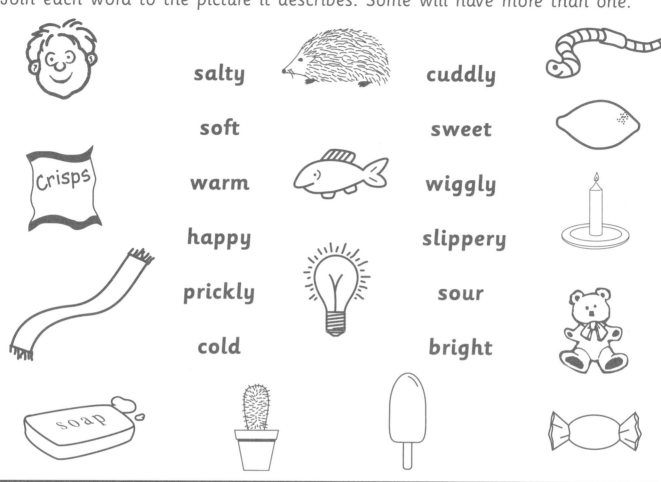

salty

soft

warm

happy

prickly

cold

cuddly

sweet

wiggly

slippery

sour

bright

B Write a sentence using two words to describe the picture.

Science 4

Magnets

A Use a magnet to attract these things.
Does a magnet attract all of them? Write **yes** or **no**.

_____ _____ _____ _____

_____ _____ _____ _____

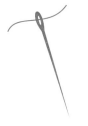

_____ _____ _____ _____

What kind of material can be attracted by a magnet?_____

Are <u>all</u> of these materials attracted by a magnet? _____

B Bury these objects in sand. Pass a magnet over the sand.

Write what happens. _____

_____

C Drop a paper clip into a glass of water. Can you get the paper clip out of the water with a magnet without putting the magnet in the water? _____ Why? _____

Number 6

A Use the number line to help you take away.

10 − 7 = ☐	18 − 2 = ☐	16 − 4 = ☐
11 − 5 = ☐	13 − 7 = ☐	20 − 10 = ☐
14 − 4 = ☐	20 − 5 = ☐	15 − 5 = ☐
12 − 6 = ☐	17 − 3 = ☐	13 − 2 = ☐
15 − 9 = ☐	19 − 6 = ☐	12 − 11 = ☐

B What time is it Mr Wolf?

☐ o'clock   ☐ o'clock   ☐ o'clock

Show the time on the clock.

4 o'clock   **12** o'clock   **7** o'clock

C What is the difference between the 2 numbers?

6 and 7 → ☐   10 and 12 → ☐   8 and 13 → ☐

3 and 5 → ☐   11 and 14 → ☐   15 and 20 → ☐

D Join the dots to make a triangle and a hexagon.

Trace over the shapes. Draw the other half.

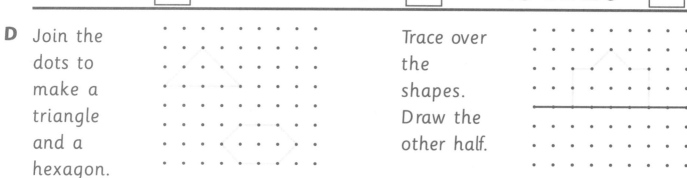

Language 8

A Some animals hatch out of eggs. Write the name of each animal below its egg.

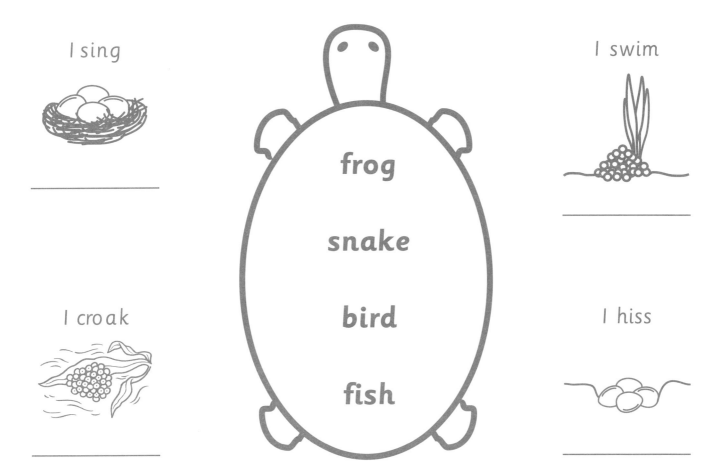

I sing

I swim

I croak

I hiss

frog

snake

bird

fish

Can you think of another animal that lays eggs? _____

B Look at the pictures. Say the word for the picture. Listen to the first sound and write it down at the beginning of the word. **sh st ch**

_ _ in

_ _ amp

_ _ ip

_ _ air

_ _ ar

_ _ eep

_ _ eese

_ _ airs

Number 7

A | Find the missing numbers.

$$10 + \boxed{} = 16 \quad\quad 5 + \boxed{} = 15 \quad\quad 20 + \boxed{} = 20$$

$$10 + \boxed{} = 12 \quad\quad 9 + \boxed{} = 19 \quad\quad 11 + \boxed{} = 16$$

$$10 + \boxed{} = 18 \quad\quad 13 + \boxed{} = 13 \quad\quad 14 + \boxed{} = 17$$

$$10 + \boxed{} = 11 \quad\quad 10 + \boxed{} = 20 \quad\quad 15 + \boxed{} = 20$$

B | Colour the coins to pay.

13p — 1p 1p 10p 20p 2p 5p

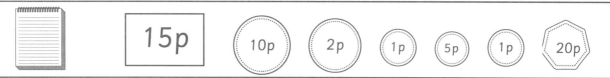

15p — 10p 2p 1p 5p 1p 20p

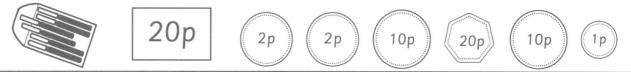

20p — 2p 2p 10p 20p 10p 1p

12p — 2p 2p 2p 1p 10p 20p

C

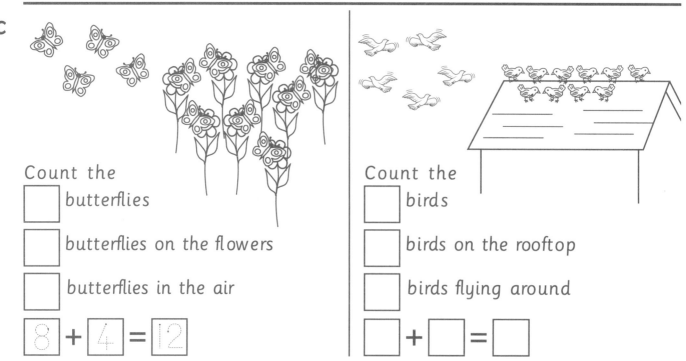

Count the
☐ butterflies
☐ butterflies on the flowers
☐ butterflies in the air
$8 + 4 = 12$

Count the
☐ birds
☐ birds on the rooftop
☐ birds flying around
$\boxed{} + \boxed{} = \boxed{}$

Science 5

A Waterproof

Materials that are waterproof keep out water. Find out which materials named on the pots below are waterproof.

Place the material over a pot and fasten it with an elastic band. Pour a spoonful of water on each, and watch!

Does the water soak through? If it does, colour the pot on the page yellow.

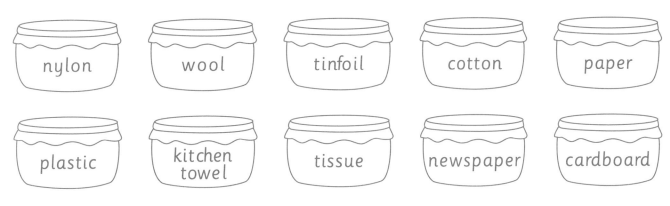

nylon   wool   tinfoil   cotton   paper

plastic   kitchen towel   tissue   newspaper   cardboard

Which materials are waterproof ?

_____

B Colour green all the objects which are waterproof. Write down the material they could be made from.

_____   _____   _____   _____

_____   _____   _____   _____

Which material would you use to make a boat?_____

Why?_____

Language 9

A Who? What? When? Where?

Write a sentence to answer the question about the picture.

Who? _____

What? _____

When? _____

Where? _____

Who? _____

What? _____

When? _____

Where? _____

B Spelling

Unjumble the letters to spell the word correctly.

ampr

loost

mudr

agfl

_____ _____ _____ _____

assgl

peesl

gofr

poch

_____ _____ _____ _____

Number 8

A Add and take away.

$16 - 7 =$ ☐ | $15 - 5 =$ ☐ | $11 - 7 =$ ☐

$12 + 4 =$ ☐ | $20 - 8 =$ ☐ | $13 + 7 =$ ☐

$5 + 6 =$ ☐ | $4 + 6 =$ ☐ | $17 - 9 =$ ☐

$19 - 6 =$ ☐ | $11 + 5 =$ ☐ | $13 - 3 =$ ☐

$13 - 11 =$ ☐ | $19 - 8 =$ ☐ | $12 + 8 =$ ☐

B Draw how much change you need.

Change from 20p

5p

Change from 20p
10p

Change from 20p

12p

Change from 20p
18p

C Days of the week

Sunday	Monday	Tuesday	Wednesday	Thursday
	Friday	Saturday		

Write the day after.

Monday _____

Sunday _____

Wednesday _____

Write the day before.

_____ Thursday

_____ Monday

_____ Saturday

Write the days of the weekend.

_____

_____

Write the day of your
birthday this year.

_____

Language 10

Read the story.

Yesterday, we saw some tracks. They came from the forest. They went round the tree. Then they went past the pond. We followed the tracks to the bin. Bang! Crash! What's that? A hungry animal is eating his dinner.

Number the tracks in order 1 2 3 4.

Answer these questions.

A horse has hooves.
Is the visitor a horse? _____

A cat has paws.
Is the visitor a cat? _____

A fox has four toes.
Is it a fox? _____

What did you see? _____
When did this happen? _____

Number 9

A Use three numbers from 1-10 to make these totals.

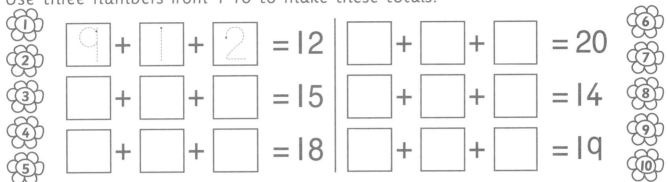

$\boxed{9} + \boxed{1} + \boxed{2} = 12$ $\boxed{} + \boxed{} + \boxed{} = 20$

$\boxed{} + \boxed{} + \boxed{} = 15$ $\boxed{} + \boxed{} + \boxed{} = 14$

$\boxed{} + \boxed{} + \boxed{} = 18$ $\boxed{} + \boxed{} + \boxed{} = 19$

B Make all money boxes add up to 20p.

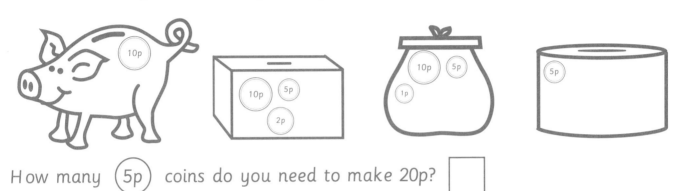

How many (5p) coins do you need to make 20p? $\boxed{}$

C Write how many tens and ones?

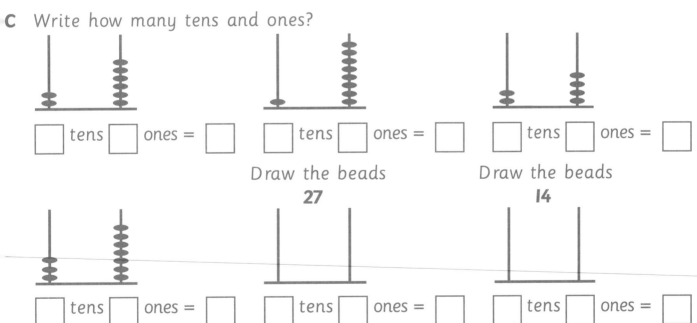

$\boxed{}$ tens $\boxed{}$ ones = $\boxed{}$ $\boxed{}$ tens $\boxed{}$ ones = $\boxed{}$ $\boxed{}$ tens $\boxed{}$ ones = $\boxed{}$

Draw the beads   Draw the beads
27   **14**

$\boxed{}$ tens $\boxed{}$ ones = $\boxed{}$ $\boxed{}$ tens $\boxed{}$ ones = $\boxed{}$ $\boxed{}$ tens $\boxed{}$ ones = $\boxed{}$

D Fill in the missing numbers.

10 20 30 ◯ ◯ ◯ 70 ◯ ◯ ◯

Science 6

A Colour
Colour the rainbow.

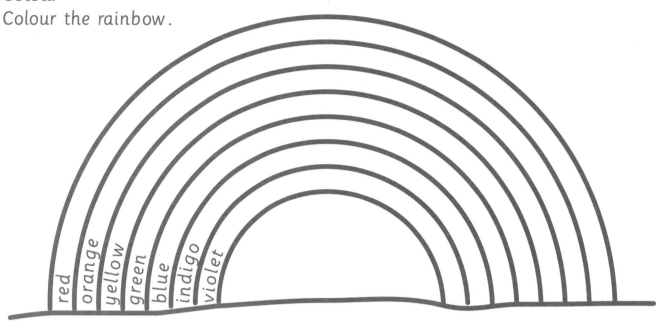

Which colour comes after yellow? _____

Which colour comes before violet? _____

B Mixing Colour
What happens when you mix these colours together? Colour and write.

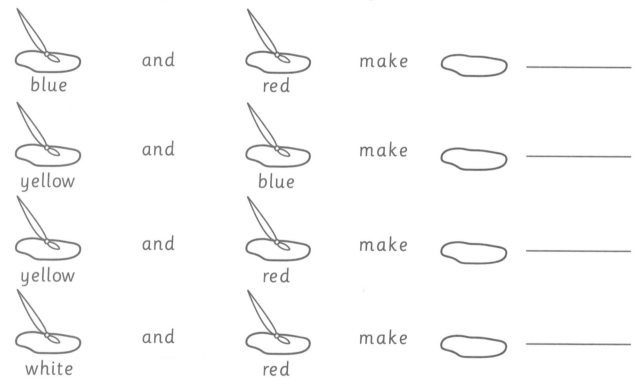

blue	and	red	make		_____
yellow	and	blue	make		_____
yellow	and	red	make		_____
white	and	red	make		_____

Try adding white to other colours. What happens?

Number 10

A A survey of cars in the car park.

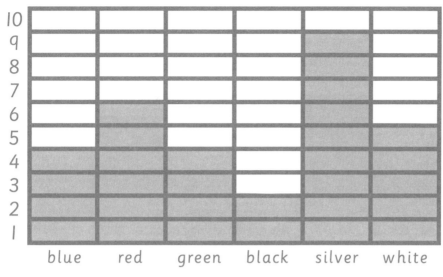

CAR COLOURS

How many cars were in the car park? ☐

How many more red cars than green cars? ☐

How many silver and blue cars? ☐

Which is the least popular coloured car? ☐

What is the difference between the number of white and silver cars? ☐

B Join pairs of numbers to make 20.

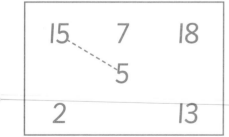

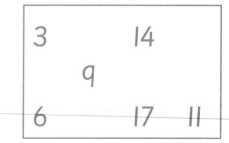

C What is the time?

   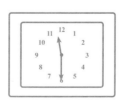 

$\frac{1}{2}$ past ☐ $\frac{1}{2}$ past ☐ $\frac{1}{2}$ past ☐ $\frac{1}{2}$ past ☐ $\frac{1}{2}$ past ☐

Schofield & Sims
HELPING CHILDREN TO LEARN

Schofield & Sims was established in 1901 by two headmasters and since then our name has been synonymous with educationally sound texts and teaching materials.

Our mission is to publish products which are:

- Good value • Written by experienced teachers
- Extensively used in schools, nurseries and playgroups
- Used by parents to support their children's learning • Educationally sound

EARLY HOMEWORK BOOK 3

A new series of four books designed to give children structured practice in English, Maths and Science. The work reinforces concepts covered in the classroom. Parental involvement is encouraged. Answers are included in each book.

Early Homework Book 1 - 0 7217 0875 7   **Early Homework Book 3** - 0 7217 0877 3
Early Homework Book 2 - 0 7217 0876 5   **Early Homework Book 4** - 0 7217 0878 1

Schofield & Sims Key Stage 1 products for 5-7 year olds

Language and literacy workbooks

Early Writing
Books 1-4
Training in letter formation, leading to joined-up writing.

First Phonics
Books 1-4
Develops phonic skills through carefully graded, enjoyable activities.

Basic Skills
Books 1-5
Helps children to achieve literacy and extend their vocabularies.

Sound Practice
Books 1-5
Structured practice in basic sounds.

Early Spellings
Books 1-3
Develops spelling skills through spelling activities, spelling patterns and establishing links between reading and writing.

Maths and numeracy workbooks

Times Tables
Books 1 and 2
Straightforward tables practice. Book 1 covers x0, x1, x2, x3, x4, x5 and x10 tables. (Book 2 is for Key Stage 2.)

Key Maths
Books 1-5
Graded maths activities for Key Stage 1.

Number books
Books 1-5
Introduces basic number skills through gently graded activities.

Posters

Sturdy, laminated posters, full colour, write-on/wipe-off, suitable for wall-mounting or desk-top use. Over 70 titles including the alphabet, numbers, colours, days, shapes, nursery rhymes, opposites, seasons, time, weather and our bodies.

Information

For further information about products for pre-school, Key Stage 1 and 2, please request our catalogue or visit our website at
www.schofieldandsims.co.uk

Author   Jane Stamford
Cover design   Curve Creative - Bradford
©2001 Schofield & Sims Ltd

Schofield & Sims

Dogley Mill, Fenay Bridge, Huddersfield, HD8 0NQ
Phone 01484 607080   Fax 01484 606815

e-mail sales@schofieldandsims.co.uk

ISBN 0-7217-0877-3

9 780721 708775

Price £1.95
Key Stage 1
Age Range 5-7 years